GEOMETRY
LESSONS
IN THE
WALDORF SCHOOL

Volume 2:
Freehand Form Drawing and
Basic Geometric Construction in Grades 4 and 5

by

Ernst Schuberth

Ａ Ｗ Ｓ Ｎ Ａ

Printed with support from the Waldorf Curriculum Fund

Published by:
The Association of Waldorf Schools
of North America
3911 Bannister Road
Fair Oaks, CA 95628

Title: *Geometry Lessons in the Waldorf School*
   Volume 2: Freehand Form Drawing and Basic Geometric
   Construction in Grades 4 and 5
Author: Ernst Schuberth
Translator: Nine Kuettel
Editor: David Mitchell
Proofreader: Ann Erwin
Cover design: Hallie Wootan
© 2004 by AWSNA
ISBN # 1-888365-52-8

CONTENTS

FOREWORD

This book is part of a multi-volume comprehensive presentation of geometry lessons in grades one through eight as taught in the Waldorf schools. Three levels are presented in light of the stages of development according to anthroposophical insights: The first encompasses grades one through three, the second grades four and five and the third grades six through eight. In his compilation of *Rudolf Steiner's Waldorf School Curriculum*, E.A.K. Stockmeyer was the first to call attention to the mirroring of the stages of development in the geometry lessons.[1]

At the first level geometry is fostered, in form drawing, as *active geometry*. The child learns to grasp and create forms in diverse ways. The child schools his or her fine motor skills and develops a feeling for the language of forms – a feeling for form is developed. At the second level the relationships of the forms to one another step into the foreground. Stockmeyer called this *comparative geometry*. At the third level begins what is commonly referred to as true geometry: *proven geometry*.

The attempt will be made with this book to present the contents and relationships of each particular level as a potential structure. I suggest the structure only as a suggestion for the independently working teacher. It would contradict the autonomy of the Waldorf school teacher if a possible way of doing something were to be dogmatically represented. I hope much more that fellow teaching colleagues will share with me their experiences and pass on suggestions to further develop this presentation.

I have many colleagues to thank whose work I encountered for varying lengths of time and at various opportunities. I would also like to thank the children with whom I was privileged to work as well as my friends in the Department of Mathematics and Astronomy at the Goetheanum. Through their long-term collaboration I have been able to acquire certain spiritual viewpoints, which have helped in my understanding of mathematics. My thanks go also to Monika Feles-Baumann, who transcribed most of the original manuscript.

Since the early nineties I have had the opportunity to work with many American class teachers and high school teachers. Their wonderful ability to feel what they think, their enthusiasm, and friendship have inspired me to continue with my nearly simultaneous working on eight books (four on geometry and four on math) for class teachers. Hopefully, I will be able to finish the last two as planned. Please send me feedback if you have interesting experiences with the book. Let me know your ideas, formulated exercises, problems, or anything else that might be important to improve the book. Last but not least I have to thank my colleague and friend David Mitchell and his team at AWSNA Publications for their tremendous work to bring forth this book, most notably to Nina Kuettel for translation and Ann Erwin for copyediting.

— Ernst Schuberth, Spring 2004
Ernst.Schuberth@t-online.de

INTRODUCTION

Somewhere around the age of ten a child goes through a spiritual transformation that puts him or her into a more conscious relationship with the environment. One of the ways the Waldorf curriculum meets this change is to have first a sorting through and discussions of the animals, then the plants and, in the sixth grade, the minerals. An age-appropriate approach to the animal and plant kingdoms is presented by relating the physical life of human beings to the animals and the soul life of human beings to the plants.

A comparative description of the simplest geometric forms such as the circle, the triangle and the square can be entered into using a similar method. The child learns to look at the individual forms consciously, to name the different forms and to differentiate particular determining factors. Thereby it does not follow that one form will lead out of another as is appropriate from the sixth grade on, but rather the forms will be placed in *comparative* relationships to one another.

The following suggested structuring can, of course, be viewed as only *one* possibility. Curriculla other than those dealt with here are thoroughly conceivable. With comparative form drawing, I am interested in having the most perfect forms (circle, square, equilateral triangle) serve as the departure point and then allowing the derived, less symmetrical forms to come out of those. I see this as corresponding to nature study in which the human being is first discussed as a kind of archetype which encompasses the individual forms found in nature.

I suggest that the elementary, basic construction tasks with compass and ruler be performed at the end of the fifth grade. I have experienced time and again with what enthusiasm the children of this age group complete the transition from form drawing and free-hand geometry to a describable construction process. This timing also creates the possibility of actually inserting proven geometry into the sixth grade.

A further interest of the following plan is the child's development of the understanding of concepts of space. If in the first grades the child has a basically flat concept of space, then during the stage of development known as the ten-year change, the child can begin to have a clearer, inner grasp of the third dimension. Even though spatial geometry (except perhaps in dealing with the regular polyhedron and simple volume calculations) is reserved for the higher grades, certainly simple observations of the relationship between light and shadow can contribute to the development of understanding space concepts. A suggestion for this is offered here only by example. Similar observations can be woven into the geometry lessons or other lesson blocks as the opportunities present themselves.

A word about the drawings: The free-hand drawings were first sketched for the most part in lead pencil and then traced over with a darker pencil. In other instances a compass and ruler were used so that the respective geometric laws which one should come as close to as possible in free-hand drawing would be more apparent. To maintain the character of a free-hand drawing, the design would then be traced with colored pencil. Some examples of free-hand drawing exercises were actually drawn for this book with compass and ruler for orientation, not as model examples.

Teachers must always take into consideration that a blackboard drawing requires totally different skills than drawing on paper. In any case, teachers should begin practice on the blackboard some time ahead. That goes for the free-hand as well as the constructed drawings. *How* the teacher draws is of fundamental importance to the children. The actual series of movements – whether the hand is calm or nervous, strong or weak pressure – makes a considerable impression that the children absorb and which determines their relationship to the subject matter!

It is advisable and helpful with difficult free-hand drawings to lightly sketch the position and important points. Success depends upon good preparation. If the teacher radiates trust in the children's abilities and leads them calmly and clearly, then the children can accomplish astounding things. However, the child is also directly schooling his or her own constitution: hand and eye coordination, fine motor skills and much else.

A considerable handicap for the printed drawings in this book is the lack of color. So we have included a CD Rom with colored drawings, supplementary exercises, and additional notes. Feel free to use whatever you like but please do not violate the rights of AWSNA or the author by printing the material or placing it on your web site without permission. The examples should stimulate your own creative abilities. Please note, however, one should avoid meaningless coloring and decorating with flowers and such things. The beauty of geometric drawings lies in the inner adherence to geometric laws that they reveal and usually penetrates much further than can be seen on the surface. In so far as the child actively and comparatively lives in the geometric world of forms, then he or she cultivates that relationship which later allows questions of knowledge to arise in the soul and leads to a truly mathematical way of looking at things.

The Fourth Grade

"And now we can move on to geometry at this age, provided we previously held that which would become geometry completely within the realm of drawing. With drawing we can develop the triangle, the square, the circle and the line for the human being. We develop the actual forms through drawing in that we draw something and then say: 'This is a triangle, this is a square.' But what appears as geometry, where we search for the relationships between the forms, that we begin only around age nine."[2]

With these words Rudolf Steiner created an impetus for form drawing in which the inner characteristics of the parallel study of man, animals and plants are presented in more detail. Especially I see an inner relationship to the methodical development of the above in producing *comparative relationships* and the drawing upon certain *archetypal forms*. So the triangle and the quadrangle come out of the circle and the common square out of the quadrangle. How this can happen on an individual basis will be shown in the following pages. Certainly only *possiblities* will be brought up here. These topics can be replaced with others or be carried more strongly into the purely artistic.

Every teacher can decide for himself where an appropriate place for geometric form drawing is in the lesson plan. For example, as a part of a form drawing block or tacked onto the end of an arithmetic block would certainly be suitable. Taking the seasons into consideration, I always found that the winter is the best time for geometry main lessons.

LEADING INTO GEOMETRY

From the Circle to the Ellipse

John[3] is called to the front of the class and asked to walk a circle. The teacher draws a circle on the blackboard and points out the connection of the walked circle to the drawn circle: "John walked around in a circle on the floor. I have also completed a circular movement with my hand, and as you were following what my hand was drawing, you also made a circular movement with your eyes. You can see the *trace* of my movement on the blackboard because I had a piece of chalk in my hand. That is how the circle came about on the blackboard. First the movement was there. With the circle you still have the *trace* of the movement; a *traced movement*."

It is important to point out the connection between the walked form and the drawing on the blackboard. Often problems with understanding will occur for the children when there is a transition from one form to another without carefully discussing the connection. The movement of the child in front of the class is experienced as a three-dimensional activity. The blackboard drawing appears to the child – especially when the drawing motion has ended – to be two-dimensional and picture-like. It loses the three-dimensional character associated with all physical activities. That is why it is important to show how this picture came out of an activity and it is grasped by looking at it which is, again, an activity – the movement of the eye.

Naturally, the children have long been familiar with the circle and it has often been done in form drawing and eurythmy. In order to now enter into a comparative observation of form, the teacher walks the circle and with the repetitions slowly stretches the length of the circle so that an *ellipse* is apparent. The children can observe the occurring changes: At each end, the curvatures get ever more pronounced and in-between ever less so. Finally, one concludes something like this: When one walks in a circle, one *walks* step by step *forward* and uniformly *turns* oneself. When one walks an ellipse then one also walks continually forward but the rotation is more pronounced on the narrow ends and less so in between. The rotation becomes rhythmic.

Fig. 1. The circle as traced movement

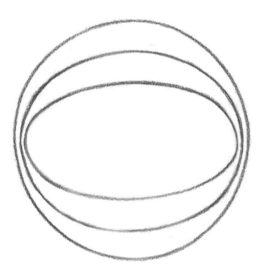

Fig. 2. From a circle to an ellipse

When walking a form one should spend some time on this turning and walking forward. Both movements can be done singly and afterward questions can be asked about the difference between the movements. Perhaps it succeeds to the point that it is said: By walking forward one's place is changed; by turning, the *direction* of one's gaze is changed.

Therefore, turning and walking forward are completely different movements. This will be well understood when the two movements are taken separately. Both movements executed together when walking a circle can cause some children problems of comprehension. In my Waldorf class in Munich it was especially a student named John who just could not see it. That he moved forward was clear, but that rotation could happen at the same time was incomprehensible to him. I had him turn in place just once more and he had to describe what he saw around him. When he had completed one rotation then he had seen all four walls. Once more he walked the circle and had to describe what he saw. This time he had also seen all four walls when the circle was completed. Somehow the whole thing remained suspicious to him. I tried again using another tack: "When you turn around one time, the other children have seen you once from all sides. Walk the circle once again and one of your classmates will describe what part of you can be seen." John did this and the child said: "Stomach, left shoulder, back, right shoulder, stomach." While John was walking the circle another child had seen him from all sides – the same as when he rotated in place.

By doing all of this the other children also became convinced that there really was something to the rotation when one walked a circular line. Only John remained mistrustful. So I said: "Go straight forward for a little way and then turn around for a while. What is the difference?" John did this and said: "Turning makes me dizzy, walking straight forward doesn't."

"Good," I said. "When one becomes dizzy when turning and one turns when walking a circle, then one must also become dizzy when walking a circle." Now John had to walk a small circle as fast as he could, and sure enough, after the fifth round he began to stagger and took his dizzily won belief that one also rotates while walking a circle back to his seat.

One can represent the *places* arrived at one after the other while walking the circle as the *points* of the circle. How should one indicate the changing directions? The teacher can ask the children to draw in the respective lines of sight one has from the individual points on the drawing of the circle on the blackboard. Something like the following picture develops (see Fig. 3a).

Here the line of sight is indicated by rays in the form of half-tangents. When that has occurred, then one can once more ask about the line of sight when the circle is walked in the opposite direction. A complete picture of the circle and its tangents comes about. (This should be treated less as geometry but rather more näively as a picture.) If the child is given a long stick to carry underneath one arm which points in the line of sight while walking a circular line, then the child can readily observe the rotation of the tangents (see Fig. 3b).

Now we can once more consider the ellipse which comes out of the circle in that we complete the drawing with tangents. When the free-hand-drawn tangents have formed approximately equal angles then their increasing numbers on the strongly curved vertexes is vivid (see Fig. 4). I highlight with colors the stronger dynamic inherent in the rotation. At the strongest curve I draw a red line, then with decreasing curvature, orange, yellow and finally green at the weakest curve. If one pays particular attention to the movement of both archetypal forms – rotation and moving straight ahead – then the experience of the differences between the circle and the ellipse further enlightens the consciousness (see the colored drawings on the CD Rom).

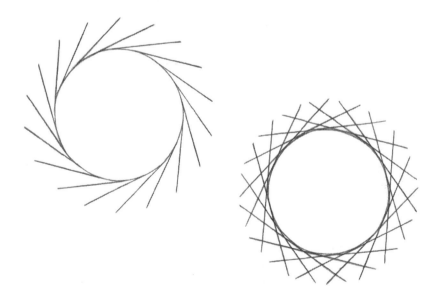

Figs. 3a – b. The circle and its tangents

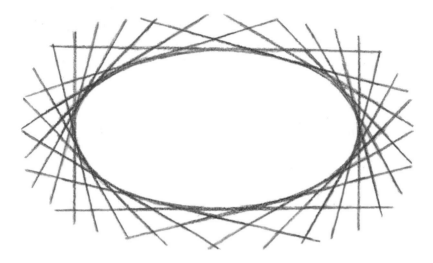

Fig. 4. The ellipse and its tangents

Now do something practical out of their experience: the children already observe the stars. Without taking away too much from the later astronomy lessons, one can describe the path of the stars in their relationships to the directions of north, south, east, and west. Some children will have already noticed that different stars are visible in the night sky at different times of the year. Perhaps one can explain at this point what would come of a more exact observation:

If one looks in the same direction at the same time every night, to the south for instance, then one sees that the same stars arrive in this directional location about four minutes earlier every day. After approximately 360 days (more exactly after 365.25 days), that is, after one year, the same stars will come back into the observed direction at the same time. So, night after night the stars in the heavens shift slightly. Ancient people used this daily shifting as a gauge for the rotating motion and because it is easier to figure with 360 than with 365.25, they chose the $^1/_{360^{th}}$ part of a full cycle of rotation as the unit for angle measurement. This unit of measurement is known as one degree and is written as 1°. While the gauge for measurement of length (meter, yard, and so forth) was taken from the fact that we walk upon the earth, the gauge for measurement of rotation originates in the heavens. It is a heavenly measure. Interesting to note at this point is: with the arm outstretched, the width of the thumb appears to be just under 1°.

The movement of the sun in the sky is also mapped out by the turning of the hands on a clock, the difference being that the small hand makes a complete revolution *twice* in twenty-four hours and not once like the sun. That is because in earlier times the measurement of time was seen as two cycles – day and night. The time between sunrise and sunset and from sunset to sunrise was divided each into twelve hours. Naturally, that made the hours in summer and winter of differing lengths. Today one can still find old church tower clocks in museums that had weights that were hung on them in the mornings and evenings so that they would go faster or slower.

The two cycles of time can be illustrated by a lemniscate (8), whereby the upper circle represents the daytime and the lower circle the nighttime. During the course of the year, the figure eight takes on a changed form. The course of a year produced a rhythmic, breathing measurement of time for people of old. Usually, a person would get up at sunrise and work until sunset. Then they would sleep. The longer working hours in the summer were compensated for by the shorter winter hours. One could say that the two time cycles have been clapped on top of one another on the face of a clock. That is why the small hand rotates around the clock *twice* in twenty-four hours.

Long ago in many places the hours were also counted differently than they are today: Sunrise was considered the *first* hour, and then followed the *second* and so on, until the *twelfth* hour which ended with sunset. Then the first nighttime hour began. The *ninth* daytime hour[5] would be from 2:00PM to 3:00PM by our terms of measurement today. The Roman Catholic Church made the time measurement rigid because of the difficulties that came about from their various religious orders and the rules of prayer, and so forth. They put the daytime and nighttime hours together and divided them into twenty-four equal parts. That is how our system of time measurement came about. This became necessary when the lands in the North, where during the summer the night is very short, could no longer follow the rules of their religious orders which required specific prayers at certain hours of the day and night.

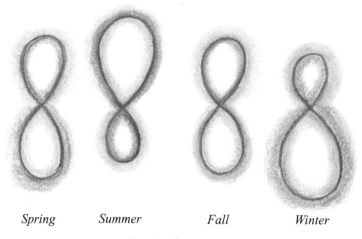

| Spring | Summer | Fall | Winter |

Fig. 5. The year in seasonal day and night cycle

Angle measurement must now be practiced by presenting angles in as many ways as possible. Here are some examples:

1. Turn around 360°, 180°, 90° and 45°.

2. Make your arms form a 90° angle (180°, 45°).

3. Show the same angles in task number 2 between your upper and lower arms.[6]

4. Two children walk at particular angles from the same starting point in different directions. Here one must pay special attention to the path of the other in order to maintain the correct angle. The smaller the angle, the slower they move away from each other.

5. Sizes of angles found in the children's surroundings are estimated.

6. Which angles can be found in the following figure (see Fig. 6).

7. Construct your own protractor (see the CD Rom).

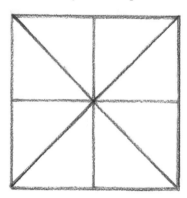

Fig. 6. Which angles can be found in this figure?

Now one can describe more precisely what the children became very familiar with in first year form drawing: There are wide and sharp angles and an angle between 0° and 90° is called an *acute* angle and one that is between 90° and 180° is called an *obtuse* angle. A *right* angle is 90°. A 180° angle is called *straight* and 360° make a *full* angle (see Fig. 7).

Obviously, here the connection to fractional arithmetic can be brought up: The unit is a full rotation cycle. One can direct the children to make a quarter-turn, a third-turn, a half-turn, and so forth, and determine the number of degrees that belong to those rotations. One degree is $\frac{1}{360}$th of a full turn.

The clock also presents opportunities to practice. Some examples for such tasks are: How many degrees does the large hand move in one minute, two minutes, three, four, five, six, ten, twelve, fifteen, twenty, thirty and forty-five minutes? How many degrees does the small hand move in these time periods? (It is always $\frac{1}{12}$th of the large hand.)

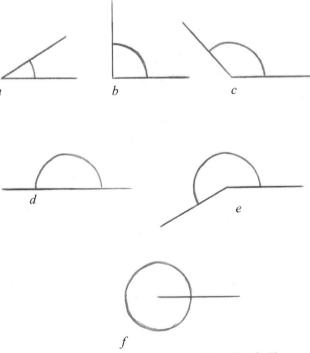

Figs. 7a–f. The various angles

Connecting fractional arithmetic to the turning of angles can also help prevent the oft-used concept of fractions as circle sectors (pieces of pie) from becoming a one-sided fixation in the understanding of fractions. It is important to avoid thinking of the angle as a circle segment. Circle segments are *areas*. Angles are formed from *directions*. Circle segments can also be different sizes but have the same angle. Depending on the size of the pie, $\frac{1}{12}$th of it could mean many different amounts of pie. Angles are completely independent of such areas or sizes of space.[7]

After an initial discussion of the angle and angle measurement has taken place and been reinforced through practice, then the angle should be examined in relation to two intersecting straight lines. Two intersecting straight lines will form four angles, that is, two identical pairs. They are called vertical angles. Two unlike angles together form a straight angle ($180°$). They are called supplementary angles. The point at which both lines intersect is the vertex for all four angles. The rays[8] which form the sides of an angle are called *angle sides*.

The question can now be raised about angles between two parallel lines. In answer, one can allow the parallel lines to form by a process of the vertex moving into infinity (see Figs. 8a–c). During this process the angle sides move more and more in the same direction. One can also point out that parallel lines always have the same direction. If one looks from one parallel line in its direction and then does the same from the other parallel line, there has been no change of direction, i.e. no rotation. Therefore, the angle between two parallel lines is zero.

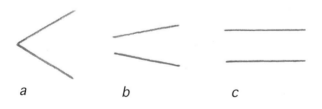

a   b   c

Figs. 8a–c. Which angles close the parallel lines?

COMPARATIVE CONSIDERATIONS OF FORM

From the Circle to the Triangle

We can transition from the circle to the triangle in a similar manner as we did from the circle to the ellipse. With that in mind, we direct a child once again to walk a circle which we lead gradually into an oval with three vertexes and finally into a triangle.

Fig 9. From the circle to the triangle

We can talk again about the rhythm of rotating and walking straight ahead. These two kinds of motion *split* in the case of the triangle. On the sides of the triangle we *move* only *forward* and at the corners we *rotate* only. Again, this can be very nicely illustrated with color (see attached CD Rom).

A wide variety of elementary free-hand geometry exercises can be done using the equilateral triangle. Indicated are possible exercises that the teacher can begin on the blackboard and the children can then continue independently.

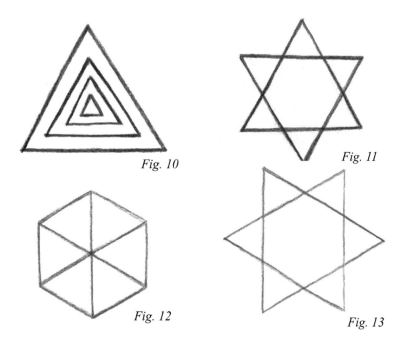

Fig. 10

Fig. 11

Fig. 12

Fig. 13

Figs. 10 – 13. Exercises using the equilateral triangle

Triangle Exercises
1. Increasing and decreasing triangles (Fig. 10).
2. Two overlapping triangles which form a six-pointed star (Fig. 11).
3. Six equilateral triangles arranged around one point so that a regular hexagon is formed (Fig.12).
4. The triangles in the hexagon opened to the outside so that a six-pointed star is formed (Fig. 13).
5. The equilateral triangle stretches (Fig. 14a), shrinks (Fig. 14b), and oscillates up and down (Fig. 14c).
6. The triangle turns curiously on its side (Fig. 15a) and oscillates to both sides (Fig. 15b).
7. A triangle with a right angle migrates with its vertex from one side to the other but always maintains its right angle (Fig. 16).

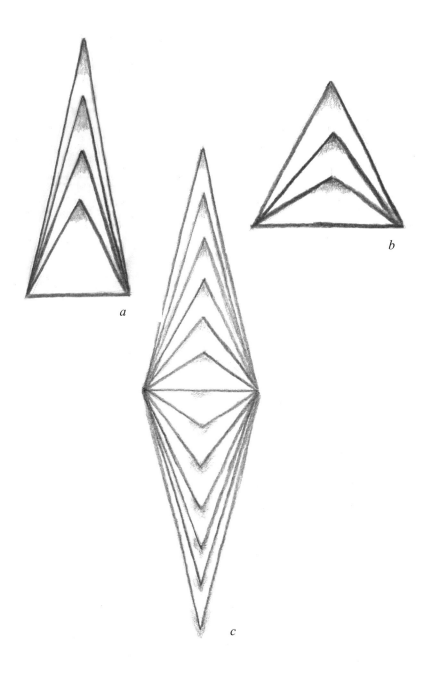

Figs. 14a–c. Exercises using the equilateral triangle

25

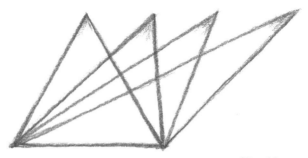

Fig. 15a

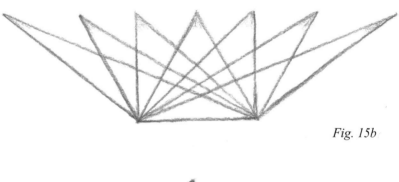

Fig. 15b

Fig. 16

Figs. 15a–b and 16. Exercises using the equilateral triangle

Lessons about the Quadrangle

Just like the triangle, the square can also be arrived at by starting with a circle and gradually converting movement. And, just as the triangle is initially transformed, we can also study the transformation of the quadrangle. Again, one can discuss how one *moves straight ahead* on the sides and *rotates* to define the angles.

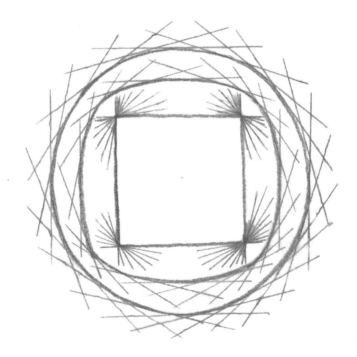

Fig. 17. From the circle to the square

In order to acquire descriptive terms for the quadrangle forms, let us begin with the symmetry of the square. That way an array of the most important quadrangle forms can be descriptively developed.

The House of Quadrangles

A square has four symmetry axes. Two go through the opposing corners and are called *diagonals*. The other two go through the opposing sides in the middle and they are called *middle lines*.

All four interior angles are the same as are all four sides. The middle lines are the same length and cut each other in half. The same goes for the diagonals. Both pairs of axes each form a 90° angle.

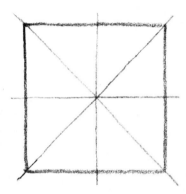

Fig. 18. The square and its symmetry axes

One can now more expertly, or more imaginatively, as has been proven desirable by comparative research, compare the variants of the quadrangle which are especially well-described through their symmetry.

For example, I tell the following story to the children accompanied by appropriate drawings:

> Mr. Square, who is considered the father of the Quadrangle race, had two quite different children. One was very conscientious, but awfully square and a little bit stiff and inflexible. His name was Rectangle. He wanted to please everyone all the time. That's why he hardly ever did anything on his own initiative. He liked best to just wait until someone told him what to do. So, he stayed simply a rectangle for a very long time.
>
> His sister was totally different. She wanted to be flexible and elegant, but because she came from the Quadrangle family, something a little angular and inelegant was still part

28

of her nature. She was named Rhombus. It seemed to Rhombus that always exhibiting right angles was too simple and rigid. That's why her angles were sometimes sharp and sometimes blunt. But, for the sake of a nice, regular figure, she always kept her sides the same length.

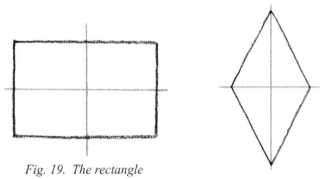

Fig. 19. The rectangle

Fig. 20. The rhombus

The siblings did a lot together, but, as siblings sometimes are, they teased each other as well. Especially when one noticed a fault in the other, then neither was shy about blurting it right out. One day when Rectangle was acting as if he were the father, Mr. Square, Rhombus laughed at him and said: "Do you want to be Father? Father has *four* symmetry axes and you have only *two*. Your diagonals are no longer symmetry axes." If you know about siblings, then you must know that they seldom will give in to the other about anything. And that was the case. After this abuse, Rectangle looked closer at Rhombus and said: "You're not any better. You *only* have *diagonals* as symmetry axes." After that both of them found that they complemented each other very well and that together they exhibited the qualities of their father.

One day their cousin, *Parallelogram,* came for a visit. You could tell they were all related because of Parallelogram's four sides and four corners, but there was no sign of a symmetry axis. At most, an axis could shine out from the center point or turn around the center point 180° one time. Parallelogram's other qualities did not seem especially desirable to the two siblings. If he saw someone else, he tried right away to make contact and adapt himself to the other, which made Rectangle and Rhombus very uncomfortable. Parallelogram even seemed to want to adapt to them: Like Rectangle, he had parallels and same-length opposite sides (that's where his name came from); and like Rhombus, his opposite angles were the same. Up to that point, his adaptation appeared pretty successful, but on the inside the two siblings thought there was something quite amiss with their cousin: Neither his diagonals nor his median lines formed a nice right angle nor were there any like-angles to be found between them. The one thing that could be said was that his diagonals and median lines bisected each other and went through the same point. So, at least Parallelogram had a correct middle point.

Fig. 21. The parallelogram

By the way, Parallelogram showed pictures of two very curious relatives. They were twin quadrangles who were created by bisecting a parallelogram. They still had one pair of opposite parallel sides, but absolutely no symmetry. They were called (common) Trapezoids. Our – somewhat proud – Quadrangles did not want to admit these Trapezoids into the House of Quadrangles because of their missing symmetry. Only after they were older did they become less proud, but that's another story.

Fig. 22. The common trapezoid

The two siblings eventually lost touch with one another. Rectangle spent a lot of time at his desk and so acquired a little middle-aged spread. He was promoted to an *equal-sided trapezoid*, but that did not help his looks any. Unfortunately, Rhombus became a little uppity. She tried to lord it over others at completely inappropriate times, and she became what you could call arrogant. Her new name – *Deltoid* or *Rhomboid* – sounded very genteel, but some people just simply called her *Kite*.

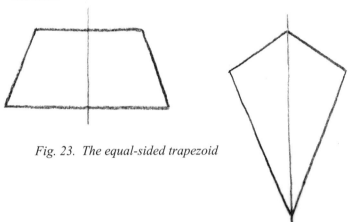

Fig. 23. The equal-sided trapezoid

Fig. 24. Deltoid, rhomboid or kite

After many years had gone by the two siblings met again at a family reunion. As much as they felt bound to one another, the changes in each other did not escape their critical notice. "What happened to you?" asked Deltoid. "You have only one single symmetry axis left." Equal-sided Trapezoid assured Deltoid: "You also have not become more beautiful." You see, this family measured beauty by their symmetry. So, the siblings once again decided that they were pretty much equal.

There's not much to tell about their later years. They met once when they were very old and just silently stared at one another because they knew that the common quadrangle didn't have any symmetry either in its simple form or its overlapping form.

Fig. 25. The common quadrangle   *Fig. 26. The overlapping quadrangle*

One can tell the following to the children as a preview of the work in the later grades:

> I want to tell you a secret that we will be talking about more fully in the sixth grade: The common quadrangles have invisibly remained squares. Maybe you can understand this a little if I draw two streets that intersect each other at right angles on a wide, flat surface. In *perspective,* which we will take up in the sixth grade, a square – the field of the street intersection – appears to be a common quadrangle and yet, you can look at a common quadrangle as a square in perspective. You see that the qualities of the father are maintained in a certain way, only more hidden. You'll learn the most wonderful things about the common quadrangle when you're in the upper grades and maybe you'll find that the square in perspective is even more beautiful and more interesting than the common quadrangle. Sometimes it's like that in the life of a human being. Young people are the most beautiful to look at. Whoever has become old and worked a lot, he or she can no longer look as nice on the outside as a younger person, but on the inside, in his soul, there lives perhaps great beauty and great riches gained by the many experiences that life has brought forth.

Such stories are perhaps not very significant in their content. One can choose many different illustrations through which the children can gain an inner relationship to the various quadrangle forms. The main thing is not to teach just definitions but rather to bring out the connections between the differing forms in such a way that something characteristic can be found in the forms and at the same time the relationship between the various forms becomes clear.

Fig. 27. Every common quadrangle is a square seen in perspective.

In summary, one can illustrate the *quadrangle family* and their relationships. It can be named *The House of Quadrangles* (see Figs. 28a–h).

Still to be explored is the fact that this family's other relatives, like the chordal quadrilaterals and the tangential quadrilaterals, who belong to another branch of the family. They will be introduced in the seventh or eighth grade.

The Most Important Characteristics of Quadrangles

The individual forms can be explored more thoroughly and their qualities characterized after the quick initial overview of the family of quadrangles. Teachers will have to decide just how far they want to go. The following table gives an overview of an array of characteristics. In the interest of brevity, each quadrangle identified with a name does not at the same time feature a higher symmetry. A square is, in fact, at the same time a rectangle. Here, however, a rectangle should be not be taken as a quadrate at the same time and the same goes for the other cases.

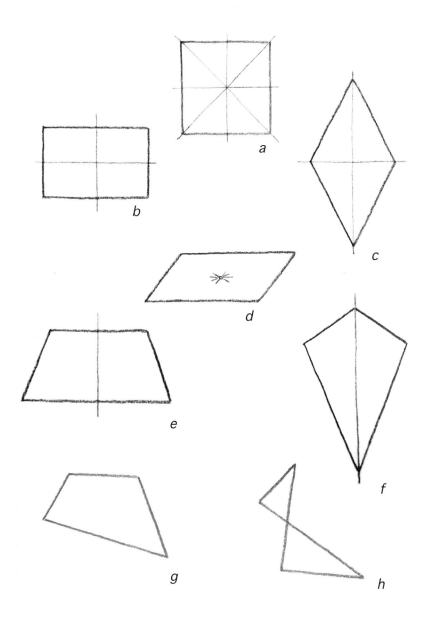

Figs. 28a–h. The House of Quadrangles

Name	Symmetry Axes	Rotation Symmetry	Angle between Diagonals	Angle between Centerlines	Ratio of Diagonals	Ratio of Centerlines	Interior Angle	Sides	Inscribed Circle	Circumscribed Circle
Quadrangle/ Square	4	90°	90°	90°	Mutual bisection	Mutual bisection	4 equal interior ∠s at 90°	4 equal sides	Yes	Yes
Rectangle	2	180°	Any	90°	Bisection	Mutual bisection	90°	2 pair opposite equal sides	No	Yes
Rhombus	2	180°	90°	Any	Bisection	Mutual bisection	2 pairs opposite equal angles	4 equal sides	Yes	No
Parallelogram	0	180°	Any	Any	Bisection	Mutual bisection	Opposite angles are equal	2 pair opposite; equal sides	No	No
Isoceles Trapezoid	1	—	Any	90°	Divided into equal but varied ratios	Mutual	2 pairs equal adjacent angles	1 pair opposite equal sides	No	Yes
Deltoid	1	—	90°	Any	One angle bisected; other divided in any way	Equal but any ratio	1 pair equal opposite angles	2 pair equal adjacent sides	Yes	No
Common Quadrilateral	0	—	Any	Any	Any	Any	Any	Any	No	No

Free-hand exercises should be carried out simultaneously with the discussions about the various quadrangle forms. The following are some suggestions for these exercises, intended to be done at the same time the respective forms are being discussed.

Quadrangle Exercises
1. Concentric squares (Fig. 29)
2. Increasing squares with a fixed point (Fig. 30)
3. Squares nested into one another (Fig. 31)
4. Rectangles inside a circle (Fig. 32)
5. From horizontal diameter[9] to vertical diameter. Rhombuses with the same symmetry axes and fixed side lengths. From a horizontal to a vertical line (Fig. 33)
6. Stars made from rhombuses with common apexes. (Figs. 34 a – b)
7. Parallelogram with the same height and base. What other quadrangle forms can be found in the drawing? (Fig. 35)
8. Star made from parallelograms (Fig. 36)
9. Isosceles trapezoid in an isosceles triangle. The trapezoid inside the triangle transforms. (Fig. 37)
10. Isosceles trapezoid over a circle chord[10] (Fig. 38)
11. Deltoid star (Fig. 39)
12. Which same-shaped fractional parts can be easily produced from the different quadrangles? Find as many examples as possible.

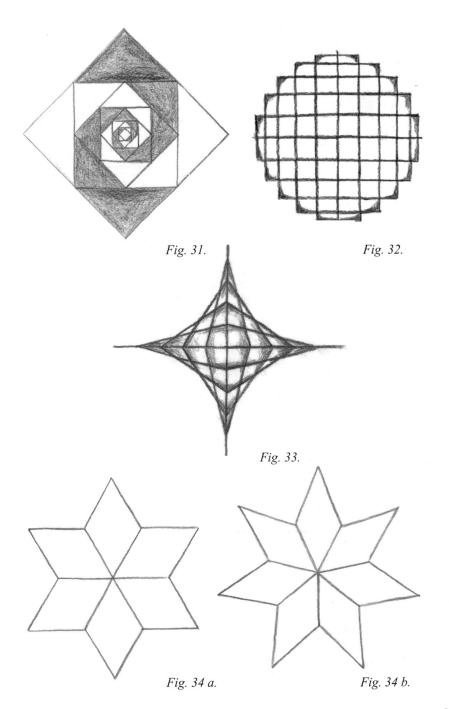

Fig. 31. *Fig. 32.*

Fig. 33.

Fig. 34 a. *Fig. 34 b.*

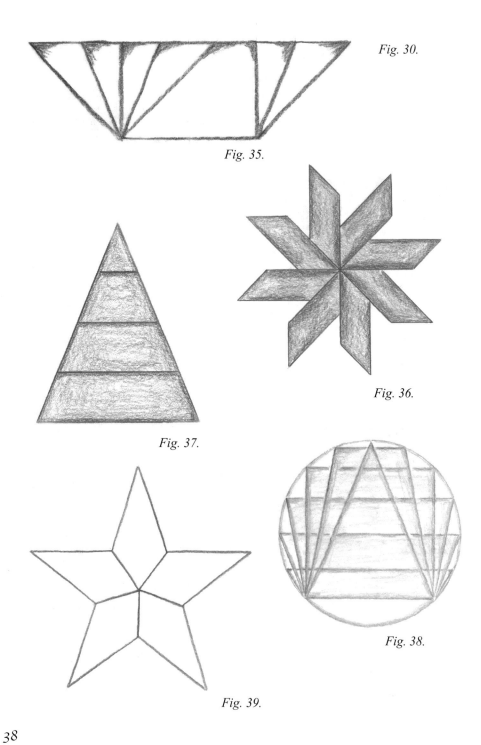

Fig. 30.

Fig. 35.

Fig. 37.

Fig. 36.

Fig. 39.

Fig. 38.

38

Light and Shadow around a Sphere

After they have crossed through the stage of development which occurs around age ten, children are mature enough to handle spatial concepts in a more inner-conscious manner than was before possible. Even though the presentation of spatial relationships through perspective drawing is first introduced in the sixth grade and constructive geometry is material for the ninth grade and higher, it is still advisable to discuss spatial forms again and again.

Contemplation of the shadow of a sphere can be an especially beautiful example. For instance, in a classroom that gets the morning sun, one can have a styrofoam ball, such as can be purchased at a crafts store, ready and waiting for an appropriate sunny day. I recommend sticking a straight pin with a plastic head on which a longish thread is attached into the ball and laying out a large piece of white cardboard. If the sun is shining and the regular lessons allow for it, then an observation of the shadow of the sphere can be incorporated into the lesson.

The ball is held up to the sunlight by the thread and the relationship between light and shadow on the ball are discussed with the children: The area of the ball turned toward the sun is lightest and gradually becomes darker until the area turned away from the sun is a shadow. The ball "answers" the sunshine with its brightness on the side turned towards the sun.

When the ball has been observed and discussed long enough, then the white cardboard is held perpendicular to the sunlight behind the ball. Just as the ball has a round contour when observed from all sides, so is the shadow also circular. If the cardboard is turned a little away from the direction of the light, then the shadow begins to lengthen. It becomes elliptical. Now the cardboard can be played through various positions. If it is bent cylindrical then the shadow loses the elliptical form and takes on still various other oval or drop-like forms. However, in the discussion one stays for now with the circular and elliptical forms of the shadow. How can a ball which is round on all sides throw an elliptical shadow?

For the time being one can bring into consciousness that one really *cannot* see light. Only where something is held up to the light can we see on that object the luminosity that is effected. But we also do not see the shadow area behind the ball. Light and dark appear only where the cardboard is placed.

Now we can talk about *light area* and *shadow area.* The sun creates light area and the ball creates shadow area. We can determine which form the shadow area has by moving the cardboard behind the ball back and forth. The shadow area is invisible, but it can be made visible by the cardboard being put nearer or further away from the ball. Even when it is itself not discernable, one can describe its form: It is cylindrical like a round pole or also like a straight sausage. The shadow comes about where the cardboard *cuts* the shadow area. If it is cut vertically to its own alignment, then, just as with a straight-cut sausage, a circular surface is created. If it is cut bias-wise then elliptical forms occur.

Shadow occurs where light and shadow areas are cut from material surfaces. In the simplest case, the shadow form depends upon the form and position of the shadow object, but also then to a large extent upon the position and form of the surface upon which we cause the shadow to appear. In reality, the form of the light-giving body, among other things, plays a role, however, that can be put off until a later time.

The children's spatial perceptiveness is extraordinarily stimulated by conducting these or similar observations in a very elementary fashion. The important thing is to not speak of abstract models such as light rays and the like, but rather deal with *formed contents of space,* their *boundaries* and *cut-out shapes.* For a blackboard drawing, there should not be lines but rather surfaces colored in with wide chalk.

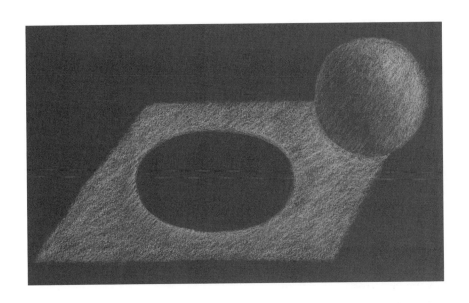

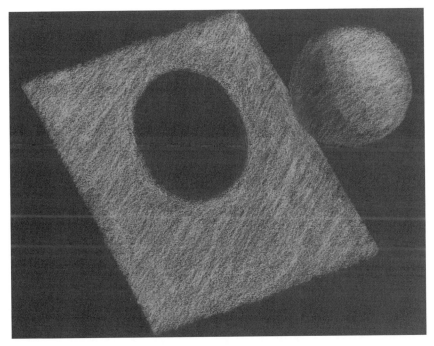

Figs. 40 and 41. The ball shadow on different surfaces

The Fifth Grade

Geometry in the fifth grade is similar to that in the fourth grade in as far as it is still free-hand geometry and viewed as an extension of form drawing. The construction descriptions suggested here belong, in a narrower sense, to the mathematics lessons.

The following geometric designs concerning symmetry should be understood, at least in part, as accompanying discussions to the free-hand exercises. The work activity time of the main lesson can begin with the consideration of the circle and symmetry. Then the daily free-hand exercises can begin in connection with which a few suggestions are given. However, for the time being, the circle should be drawn and discussed in a new way.

The Circle

One can start out with the circle form just like in the fourth grade. However, this time it should come about through a *process*. We imagine a spring out of which we allow, for instance, with yellow color, a little circular area to come out. In a second drawing we allow from around it, for instance, with blue color, also a circular form to come about to envelop the first form. Now the children should alternate between yellow and blue on both drawings so that the yellow area, always *filling* a circle form, grows toward the outside, while the blue area, *enveloping* from the outside, constricts itself to the middle, enclosing a circle form.

Let the children experience the polar feelings associated with being in the center or on the periphery, e.g. when we extend our consciousness out to the environment.

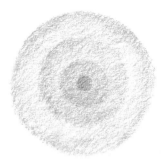

Fig. 42. Circle area expanding
Inner circle fills the form

Fig.43. Circle area enclosing
Outer circle envelops the form

Figs. 42 and 43. Inner and outer area of a circle

In a third drawing we let both processes take place at the same time. With yellow the children let a growing circle *area* come about and with blue, from the perimeter, a *hull* or *envelope* for the circle. A *circle line* comes about where the two processes meet.

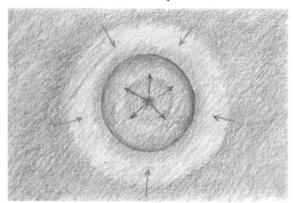

Fig. 44. Inner and outer circles meet together at the circle line

One can think of water currents which flow against one another as happens in a storm on the coast. The *surf line* comes about by the clashing of the outgoing and incoming water. That is how the circle form here is permeated with dynamic perceptions. It comes about as a result of *dynamic processes,* as a surf line of the two *currents.* It does not have a state of being in the same way as an area. Its state of being is constituted by a *process.*

The two movements can also be explored through the two mono-color drawings. The yellow can expand and contract, flow out and concentrate. The movement gestures are *distending* and *compacting*. The blue hull can enclose more tightly or expand. The movement gestures are *enveloping* and *dilating*.[11]

Straight Lines and Points as Determinants of a Circle's Boundaries

In the fourth grade we let the various forms (ellipse, triangle, square) come out of a circle. At that time we point out two kinds of movement (moving straight ahead = change of place and rotation = change of direction). The circle lines appeared as points and as a collection of rays.[12]

We can take this up again in the fifth grade. We call attention to the fact that a circle has many *places* (= points) that one can walk through and just as many *directions* that are indicated by the lines which envelop the circle as *tangents* (see Fig. 45). We can reiterate the contents of the fourth grade lessons by having a child walk a circle form and present the complete movement on the blackboard as a drawing. After that is completed, then we have the child walk the circle making it smaller and smaller until the circle has shrunk to a point and the only movement left is rotating on the point. A *pencil of lines* has come about. This consists of a point and all the lines that pass through it. The lines can rotate on this point in two ways: clockwise and counterclockwise (see Fig. 46).

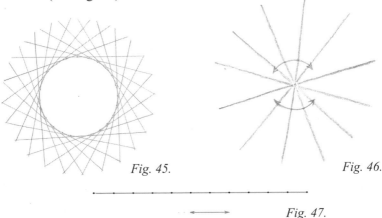

Fig. 45.   *Fig. 46.*

Fig. 47.

Figs. 45–47. A circle with its tangents can degenerate into a pencil of lines and a row of points.

45

Now we let the circle grow again. It can be said that the pencil of lines radiates out. As the circle gets bigger and bigger, then walking straight ahead becomes more apparent and rotating less so. Finally the circle becomes so big that it can no longer be walked in the classroom or drawn on the blackboard. However, we can develop the enlargement of the circle in the imagination of the children and propose that the circle grows into infinity. Of the two movements, only walking straight ahead on the single remaining line is left (see Fig. 47). A line with its points is called a *point row*.[13] As far as possible one should discuss with the children the two borderline cases of a circle – the pencil of lines and the row of points – in their polarities. Should the inner and outer parts of the circle be put into relationship with one another in the simplest way, then one can think that every point appears to be finite. That is why we had the yellow circle area expand itself out of the inner point of the spring. Every line is already infinite within itself. Lines can *envelop* a circle form like a mantle around what the points have formed by *filling out*. The entirety of the lines on the outside of a circle is called a *hull* in mathematics (see Fig. 48). The inner part formed by points is called the *kernel* (see Fig. 49). It is usually described as a circle area.

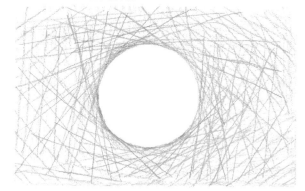

Fig. 48. Circle – outside – hull

Fig. 49. Circle – inside – kernel

46

Points and Straight Lines in Relation to the Circle

We can draw the children's attention to the polar relationship of points and straight lines to a circle based on the preceding considerations. The word *polar* demonstrates that something opposed, but still oriented to the other, is acting, just as can be observed in the simplest case with the north and south poles of a magnet. One can tell the children that these polar relationships will be explored still further, in the upper grades (tenth or eleventh) and in much more detail.

A special point in a circle is the *center point*. The lines going through the center point are called the *center lines*. They cut the circle into opposite points on the circle. The (line) segments between such opposite points is called the *diameter* of a circle. The half-diameter, that is the distance from the middle point to a point on the circle, is called the *radius*.

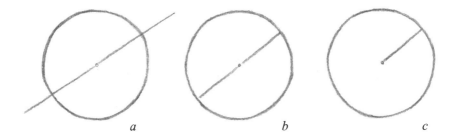

a b c

Figs. 50a – c. Center line, diameter, radius

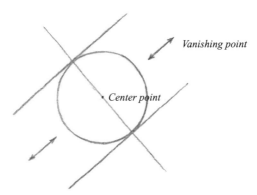

Fig. 51. The relationship of the center point to infinity

If one observes a center line and the tangents at their point of intersection with a circle, then these tangents are *parallel*. They point out into infinity. So, the center point of the inner circle stands in a relationship to infinity, out of which comes the hull that we sketched as blue in the beginning, which then expands itself toward the middle. The center point of a circle with all its center lines is the equivalent of infinity in all directions.[14]

Now, when a straight line gradually approaches a circle line out of infinity, we can describe various locations in relationship to the circle. As long as a straight line does not meet or touch a circle, it is called a *passant*. If it touches the circle then it becomes a *tangent*. If it cuts the circle in two points it is a *secant*. If it goes through the center point then, as we have already said, it is a *center line*. The relationship of straight lines to a circle is essentially determined by the number of circle points. Here also the *chord* should be defined: It is the segment of a secant which is determined by the circle points of intersection.

One can differentiate between the points, now, according to how many straight lines they have in common with the circle (see Figs. 52 a–h). The following terms, except for the boundary point, are not common but they do correspond exactly to the distinction between the different locations of the straight lines. A point on the inside of a circle has no tangents in common with the circle. It corresponds with the passant which has no points in common with the circle. One could call it an *avoidance point*. Now, if the point advances to the outside, then it comes to lie on the circle line and has a straight line in common with the circle, a tangent. It is called a boundary point. The secant with its two circle points corresponds to a point on the outside of the circle which now has two straight lines (tangents) in common with the circle. One could call it a *connection point*. The center lines would correspond to a point that is infinitely far-off and sends two facing tangents to the circle just like the center line has two parallel circle points. One could call it a *vanishing point*.

I do not consider it necessary to introduce all of these terms. However, one should call attention to the facts of polar relationships between straight lines and points of the circle.

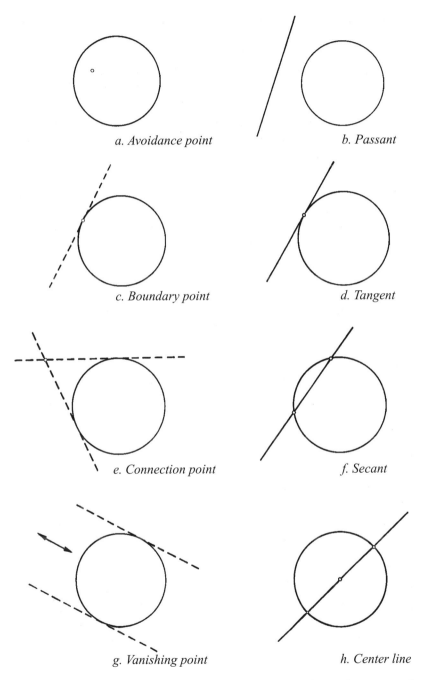

a. Avoidance point

b. Passant

c. Boundary point

d. Tangent

e. Connection point

f. Secant

g. Vanishing point

h. Center line

Figs. 52a–h. Points and straight lines in relationship to a circle

Circle Symmetry

The children have long been familiar with axis symmetry through a wide variety of form drawing exercises. Considering the significance of understanding symmetry to the development of geometry, here one can especially make note of symmetry relationships of the circle and the simple figures connected with that, taking care not get into formal systematics too soon. Along with that the teacher can one day discuss (axis) symmetry and perhaps at that time specify one of the simple figures of axis symmetry. For instance, during discussions about the quadrangle, symmetry axes belonging to the House of Quadrangles were brought into the discussion. One or the other of these figures could be recalled.

Then one could ask the children about the symmetry axes of a circle. The result will probably be found very quickly: All center lines – and only those – are symmetry axes (see Fig. 53).

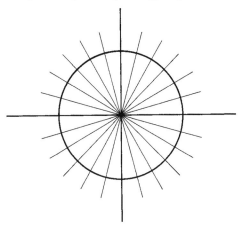

Fig. 53. All center lines – and no other straight lines –
are symmetry axes of a circle

Now let us have a second, same-size circle emerge from the first whose center point is shifted (see Fig. 54a). This new figure consisting of two circles has only *two* symmetry axes left: The connecting line of both circle middle points and the connecting line of both circle intersection points. The two symmetry axes are perpendicular to one another.

Now if the centers of the circles spread further apart then we have a case of both circles coming into *contact* (see Fig. 54 b). The one symmetry axis is then the common tangent. If both center points spread further apart, then the second axis goes perpendicular to the connecting lines of the circle middle points – in the middle between the circle middle points (see Fig. 54 c).

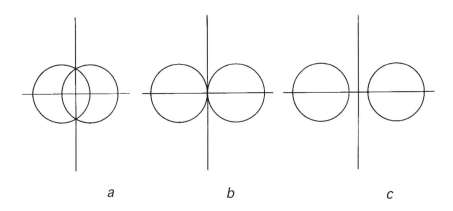

a   *b*   *c*

Figs. 54 a–c. The symmetry axes of two circles with the same radius

Now we can vary the figure in another way by allowing the circles to become ever smaller (see Figs. 55 a–c) until they finally shrink to a point: Even the very simple figure made of only two points has two symmetry axes (see Fig. 55 c).

In a further variation we let the circles grow ever larger until they finally become lines (see Figs. 55 d–e).[15] If they are parallel (see Fig. 55 e) then the very interesting case appears in which there are again very many symmetry axes to be found, and, in fact, all the straight lines that go parallel to the original connecting lines of the center points have become symmetry axes. The original second symmetry axis is now a middle parallel. However, if the two straight lines intersect one another, then there are only two symmetry axes in the figure (see Fig. 55 f).

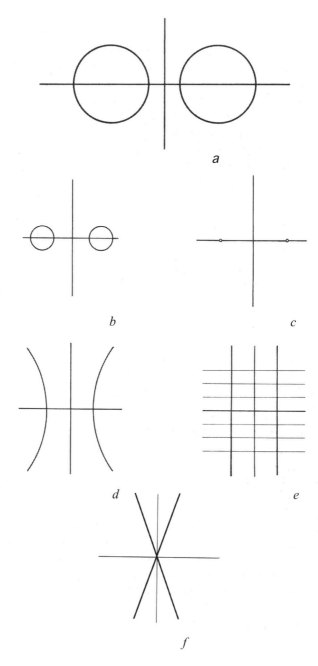

Figs. 55a–f. Symmetry of two circles plus the threshold cases

The metamorphosis of the figure can progress interestingly in that we now vary the circle radii (see Figs. 56b–c, and 56d–e). Then the connecting line of both circle middle points is the only symmetry axis.

Again, we can vary the figure to the extreme where only points and straight lines appear (see Fig. 56 f). When the point does not lie on the straight line, then the figure made of one point and one line has exactly one symmetry axis. The case of a circle and one of its intersecting lines (a secant) should also be specially mentioned. The symmetry axis runs perpendicular to the associated chord and bisects it (see Fig. 56 g).

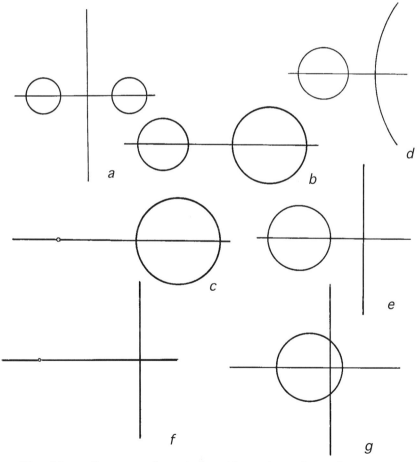

Figs. 56a–g. Symmetry of two circles with varying radius and extreme cases

Freehand Geometry Exercises

The discussions that have taken place about the circle should be accompanied by freehand geometry exercises. Some of the exercises have perhaps been done in previous years. However, they can always be put into a new light and show, in their increasing perfection, something of the progress made by the children. Additionally, such exercises can be constructed when the compass and ruler are introduced. Through this the abilities of the hand as well as the accuracy of the instruments are shown in reciprocal illumination.

1. A circle (Fig. 57)
2. Concentric circles formed from inside to outside the reverse (Fig. 58)
3. Germinal exercise (Fig. 59)
4. Balance between a point and a line by a group of circles (Fig. 60)
5. Triangles in a circle (to practice flexible perceptions and comparative descriptions) (Figs. 61a–b)
6. Circle rosette (Fig. 62)
7. Five-pointed star in a pentagon (Fig. 63)
8. Squares nested together (Fig. 64)

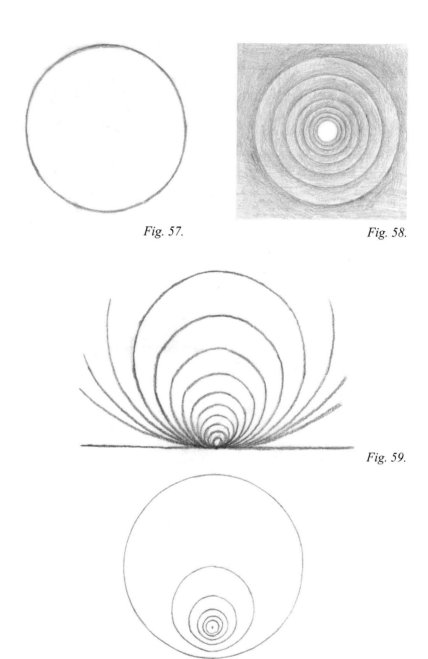

Fig. 57.

Fig. 58.

Fig. 59.

Fig. 60.

Figs. 57–60. Freehand geometry exercises

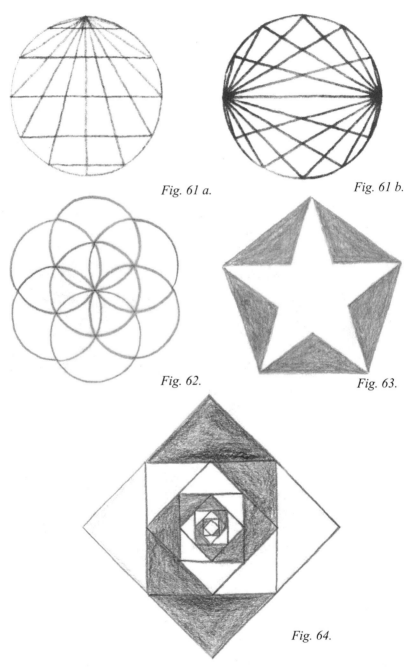

Fig. 61 a.

Fig. 61 b.

Fig. 62.

Fig. 63.

Fig. 64.

Figs. 61–64. Freehand geometry exercises

Introduction to the Compass and Ruler

The introduction of the compass and ruler not only makes available tools for more exact drawing, but these tools are at the same time the expression of certain concepts and concept correlations that lead to totally new tasks and questions. For instance, it makes no sense in freehand geometry to ask about the construction of the middle point of a line segment. If the centers of the sides are determined, as in the nested squares exercise, then schooling of the senses and coordination takes place. In contrast, if a compass and ruler are available, then certain actions are pre-determined by the tools. Those applications can be conceptually described and thoughtfully justified. Motor skill development through the use of the instruments begins to separate itself from mathematical *content* as is apparent by the use of a computer geometry program where an extreme separation of motor-activity and the content presented on the monitor can come about.

A parent evening should take place well in advance to prepare for the introduction of geometric instruments. There one should ask in which homes appropriate compasses and drawing apparati are available. These tools should be labeled with children's names and brought to school so that the teacher has enough time to look at them and decide whether they are usable. If an order is necessary, it is recommended that it be a combined order carried out by the teacher. As a standard, the legs of a compass should be so well connected that they can only be moved together. For larger drawings, it is useful to get a compass that can be extended. Besides being well-equipped, one should have a graduated 12-inch ruler, a set square, pencil, colored pencil, pencil sharpener and a piece of fine sandpaper to sharpen the compass lead. Felt-tip pens are not appropriate for geometric drawing because they bleed through the paper. Until the beginning of constructive geometry, every child should have at least a compass and ruler ready in the supplies closet in the classroom. Besides the line-free lesson books, I like to have larger drawing paper on hand for larger drawings for which the children have folders or portfolios.

When the first day of constructive geometry lessons arrives, it is advisable to have all the drawing apparati ready but not yet handed out to the children. First the teacher should demonstrate on the compass all the parts it has and how one handles it. One calls attention to the compass point which can be easily bent if it falls to the floor which can really ruin the compass. One names both *legs* of the compass and demonstrates how the point and lead are put in and taken out, what problems can occur if one of the fastening screws is lost, how one sharpens the lead with sandpaper wedge-shaped (not round), and finally, how one properly holds the compass and draws a circle:

The compass leg with the steel point is taken in the left hand. The right hand holds the compass grip (left-handed children do the opposite). The left hand places the steel point where the circle center point should be, presses it lightly and releases (see the photo on the attached CD Rom). The right hand turns clockwise on the grip so that the space between the compass legs is as perpendicular to the paper as possible. It can also tend lightly forward in the direction of movement. The above described handling of the compass for drawing would be best demonstrated with a large blackboard compass.

There is very little to say about the ruler. As the teacher runs his or her finger over the drawing edge, the smoothness should be described. The danger is that if the ruler falls or is struck, it can get a nick on the edge and then it is useless for exact work. After the tools have been handed out, the children can see for themselves the quality of these instruments.

This loving and comprehensive discussion of the instruments results in the children's being much more careful with them. Teaching the value of a good tool cannot be over emphasized.

Terms

If, out of the lessons, a need arises to succinctly express oneself about drawing, then terms for vertexes (points), sides, straight lines and angles of figures should be systematically discussed. It can be done in the normal, traditional way or also somewhat differently. We designate points with large Latin letters, lines with small Latin letters and angles with small Greek letters. These designations are still today widely in use, even in countries that otherwise do not use Latin or Greek script. That is why, for instance, it is not all too difficult to orient oneself to a Russian geometry book.

In later years we will learn to denote straight lines by specifying two points: AB. AB is the connecting line segment between points A and B. $\overline{AB}$ is the mathematical way of designating the line segment between points A and B.[16]

Straight Line and Circle Exercises

The children should become familiar with the newly-introduced drawing instruments through a series of simple exercises. From the beginning, the teacher and the children should pay close attention that the work is exact. The pencils with lead that is not too soft should be well sharpened. If a circle middle point is on a straight line or circle border line, then the accuracy must be more than one-sixteenth of an inch. Before drawing begins, the circle's center point should be marked so that it can be easily found again. This is especially important when drawing on the blackboard. The circle rosette or the circle rosette fields will quickly show how accurately the work is being done. A series of suggestions are given in the drawings here which can be easily expanded.

If points are to be marked at even intervals on a straight line, then it is often better to use a compass with two points (instead of pencil lead) because when you have put down one point, then the next one is already there to be marked. Of course, there are instances where the use of graduated rulers is beneficial, but it generally leads to inexact results.

Drawing Exercises Using Compass and Ruler

(The children can add color to these drawings as they wish.)
1. The simple circle (Fig. 65).
2. A group of concentric circles grows in equal intervals. For this, first of all, the same intervals will be marked off on a line (Fig. 66).
3. A circle rosette (Fig. 67). With exact drawing the rosette closes itself. A proof will follow in the sixth grade. This exercise can be expanded into rosette fields. Besides that, many straight-lines figures can be discovered within it. For instance, the most varied square and triangle forms can be found in it. Especially also the regular hexagon can be constructed in a circle.
4. Points are marked on a vertical straight line in equal intervals. Choose a suitable point for the middle and draw circles around the other points through this middle (Fig. 68).
5. Draw only every other leaf of a circle rosette. Connect all the points together and with the center point (Fig. 69).

6. Draw a circle around a point and four more circles out of the rosette so that you can draw-in a right angle (Fig. 70). *Solution:* Draw a circle and to it a horizontal center line. With it the perpendicular is to be constructed. Draw around the point of intersection of the center line with the circle, two circles with the radius of the first. Continue as shown in the drawing.

7. Starting from the vertex, equal lines are repeatedly marked on the legs of an angle. The point elements are connected as shown (Fig. 71).

8. A right angle can be constructed using the figure from Exercise 5. One can also construct a square from it. In a square with 3-inch side lengths, the point elements are now marked in half inch intervals on the sides. A circle with the same radius is drawn around each point element. When different children choose different radii, then together a beautiful metamorphosis series can be created. Of course, the square and the intervals of the point elements can be varied in the choosing. In general, it is beneficial to begin with a right angle and, starting from the vertex, mark the interval lengths as often as desired on both angle legs. Only then should the square be completed (see Fig. 73).

9. As in the Exercise 8, a square is constructed with equally divided sides. The point elements are then connected together as shown (see Fig. 73).

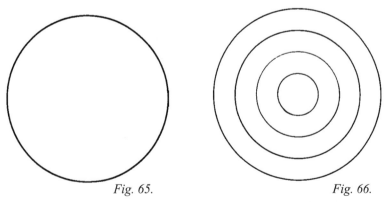

Fig. 65.   *Fig. 66.*

Figs. 65–66. Straight line and circle exercises

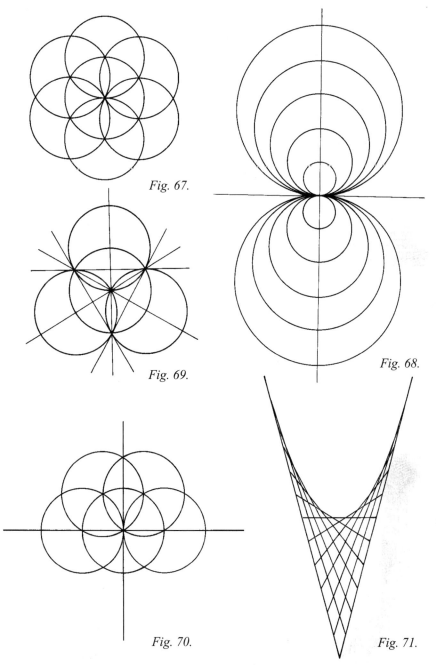

Fig. 67.

Fig. 69.

Fig. 68.

Fig. 70.

Fig. 71.

Figs. 67–71. Circle and straight line exercises

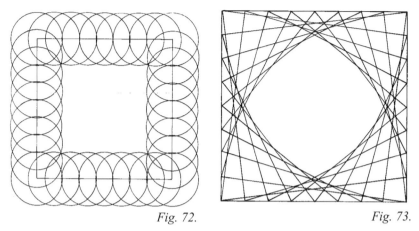

Fig. 72.   Fig. 73.

Figs. 72–73. Circle and straight line exercises

BASIC GEOMETRIC CONSTRUCTIONS

Methods

When the handling of the drawing tools has been adequately practiced, then basic construction can begin.Dealing completely with a geometric construction exercise includes a series of steps which can be short, or almost blend into another step, or even be skipped occasionally, but they all belong to the full answer. Louis Locher-Ernst describes these steps as follows:

Learning mathematics includes a large amount of problem-solving. Unfortunately, too little emphasis is given to at least some of the problems being *completely* solved. A really complete solution takes a lot of time. The steps taken in solving problems experienced in this way are unforgettable to those who have gone through them. I will briefly characterize the process of such a solution. It's about any geometric problem (for example, the construction of a square from given data). The problem immediately presented contains very *definite* points (for example, not only the "angle between the diagonals," but also its required size). That is why the Greeks spoke of the *protasis,* the general problem, and the *ekthesis,* the definite problem. In the next step, the *solution (analysis)* has to do with building a bridge from that which is given to that which is sought. A certain amount of mathematical imagination is necessary. Further, the bridge will make it much easier to find the more relevant mathematical truths which can then be lifted into the consciousness. Once the fundament of the bridge has been made then one goes to the fourth step, *leading back (apagogae),* according to the result of the third step, when one takes the presented problem back through a chain of known, simple, basic steps. The course from a general problem to the leading back proceeds *analytically*: The general problem is peeled out of its real-world context, stripped and dissected. A natural rest period occurs. A turning point occurs in which the further steps change their direction. The fifth step consists of the *construction (kataskeuae).* In accordance with the leading-back, each warranted construction is *really* done. The next step, the *proof (apodeixis),* has to show that the completed construction renders enough of the requirements, put in place by the presented problem, in all its components. Essentially, what happens is that the analysis is gone through in reverse order. Review and preview, take place in the last step, the *result (diorismos).* The different possibilities of the general problem, which are partly excluded through ekthesis, should be taken into consideration as far as possible and these possibilities should be examined for their various consequences. Most of the time new problems come up as a result. The circle is thereby closed. Taken as a whole, the course from the above mentioned rest period, is synthesizing. It ends with the integration of the dissected problem into the context within the world of ideas.[17]

For pedagogical uses, this series of steps is complemented if attention is paid to a right anchoring of the subject matter in the soul of the child. The chronology can be described like this:

1. Pathway leading to questions that pose problems to be solved. This often happens through a short story in which a life-situation is brought to the children's attention.

2. The working out of the mathematical problems
3. The specific, presented problem
4. Solution of the problem
5. Description of the solution
6. Why is it correct?
7. Simplified construction for daily, skillful use
8. Illustration of associated wholeness through a beautiful drawing
9. Use of construction with the most varied problems
10. Expansion of the problem
11. Posing of new questions

In the construction of a perpendicular bisector of a given line segment the progression of steps will be presented in a simple form. If one goes through these steps with the children, then it can be experienced how a child, first of all, becomes connected to the world under a certain aspect. Then the children draw to themselves what they already know from the geometry lessons. In the solution, a child's entire individual strengths are called upon. In the description and explanation of the construction, the child brings every single step into consciousness. Out of this narrowness a gradual expansion again turns the soul-view towards larger connections and new questions.

1. Basic Construction: The Perpendicular Bisector

Leading to the problem

One can, for instance, tell the children about two very dangerous, chained dogs, A and B, whose places are marked on the blackboard with A and B. A child, who is a little bit afraid, has to make his or her way between them. How will the child go? In general, children will name the perpendicular bisector of a line segment $\overline{AB}$.[18] On this bisector path, the child will maintain equal distance from the dogs. This perpendicular bisector is the symmetry axis between the two points.

Working through mathematical problems

It will be noted that a line whose points are always equally distant from two other points often have a special significance in geometry or with practical problems in life. The expressions *line* and *perpendicu-*

lar bisector will be used. How can the perpendicular bisector of a given line be constructed using a compass and ruler?

The solution

The solution will generally be found by the children independently. Different solution suggestions will be listened to and discussed. The discussion will be continued until a general understanding and agreement is reached.

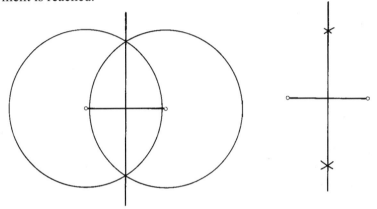

Figs. 74 and 75. Construction of the perpendicular bisector

Description of the construction

Here the children should have enough time to give a description of what they *do* in order to construct a perpendicular bisector of a line. We are not yet concerned with having the shortest, stenographer-like formulation. For many of the children, the handwork-like character of the handhold to be implemented still stands in the foreground. One can learn much about the children by carefully going into their individual descriptions. For example, a child could write:

> I open the compass until it covers more than half the line. Then I stick the compass point into end point A of the line and draw a circle around point A. I do the same thing with the other endpoint B of the line. Both circles cut themselves in two points. With the ruler I now connect these two points and get the desired perpendicular bisector of line $\overline{AB}$.

If one compares this comprehensive description to something like this short definition: "Two circular arcs around A and B, with the same radius r > $\overline{AB}$/2 are brought to intersection at two points; the connecting line is the desired perpendicular bisector of $\overline{AB}$." One can see that the second description is certainly also precise, but it leaves the actual process hardly any more visible. For a lot of hands-on oriented children, geometry is thus made abstract and incomprehensible.

Explanation of the construction

All the points of a circle are the same distance from its center point. Since both circles around points A and B have the same length radius, both symmetry axes of the circles go through their points of intersection including their middle points, just as we have already discussed.[19]

Simplified construction

For the daily, skillful application of construction it is enough to draw only short circular arc segments, rather than a full circle, which an eye measurement will estimate where they will intersect. This is, above all, necessary when the construction itself plays a secondary role and the main object is the perpendicular bisector.

One can make a little contest with the children to see who can construct a perpendicular bisector with the smallest circular arc segments and without using an eraser.

The whole and the transition to new questions

In order to demonstrate the construction belonging to the whole in a beautiful drawing, one can use sequences of circles which all lead to the perpendicular bisector. A totally new set of questions arises if one lets the circles grow around both end points of the line equally, then a field of intersecting circles comes about whose points intersect.

In order to accomplish the construction in a practical manner, it is best to draw a horizontal straight line which is, for example, divided into half inch-long line segments. We mark off the endpoints of the line segments in quarter inch intervals, around which we now draw circles growing evenly on the right and the left. If one colors in the resulting area segments like a checkerboard, then it becomes visible that the perpendicular bisector is a special case within a whole group of curves that can be found in this field (Fig. 76). In the eighth grade the ellipses and hyperbolas contained within will be studied more closely.

The task of constructing a perpendicular bisector should not be ended without also putting the line in different positions. The expression "perpendicular" will naturally at first be associated with the vertical plumb direction. "Perpendicular to a line segment or straight line" however, always means that between the given line and the constructed perpendicular a *right angle* is formed and it can also form if the two lines are in different positions. Herein is an important advancement that is characteristic of this age group: Now begins the possibility to separate spatial forms from their spatial positions and to grasp, for instance, standing vertical as a quality that can be independent of its position.

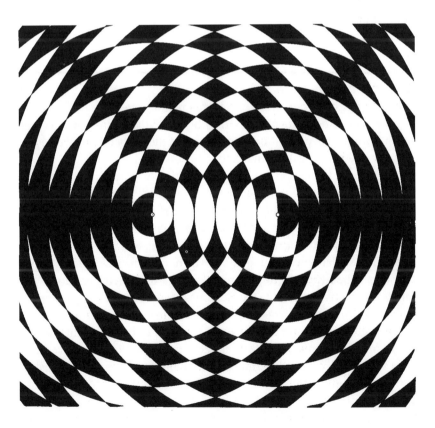

Fig 76. Groups of circles which lead to the same perpendicular bisector

Perpendicular Bisector Exercises

1. Draw a diameter in a circle and construct the perpendicular-standing diameter for it. Describe the construction.
2. Use the first exercise to construct a square in a circle. Describe the construction.
3. Construct an octagon in a circle. Use the second exercise for it. Describe the construction.
4. Construct a regular hexagon in a circle and erect the perpendicular bisectors on all sides of the hexagon. Search for as many interesting geometric figures as possible that can be found in this figure or that can be easily constructed with their help (dodecagon, twelve-pointed star, six-pointed star, square, triangle, etc.).
5. Construct an equilateral triangle with side lengths of two and a half inches.

2. Basic Construction: Bisecting a Line

From the basic construction above, making a perpendicular bisector, there is also another problem to be solved; bisecting a line segment. For this, only the intersection point of the perpendicular bisector with the given line is to be marked.

In the practical application, one should choose relatively large radii for the circles needed to construct a perpendicular bisector so that both intersection points are far enough apart to allow the connecting straight line to be drawn reliably. Normally, with the bisection of a line, one lets the two accompanying circles intersect close to the given line because that way an adequate measure of accuracy is achieved.

Tip: When constructing on the blackboard, the teacher should estimate as exactly as possible the half-line distance as the compass opening and, starting from the two endpoints of the line, mark it on the line. Usually there is a slight discrepancy. The center is marked according to eye measurement. This is faster because a ruler does not have to be used again and, within the context of drawing accuracy, it is at least as good as a lengthy construction.

Exercises on Bisecting a Line

1. Construct a square in a circle. Bisect the four sides of the square and connect the points again to a square. Draw the diagonals in this square and assemble a square within a square so that the corners of the following square are always on the side-middle of the previous square. Color in parts of the figure to create interesting designs. An example of this is given in the following drawing (see Fig. 77).

2. Construct the corresponding figures with regular hexagons[20] (see Fig. 77 and the figures on the attached CD Rom).

3. With our knowledge gained thus far, it is also now possible to construct a regular pentagon within a given circle (Fig. 78). For this the following construction steps are to be carried out:

- Draw the given circle in which the pentagon will be drawn.
- Draw a diagonal.
- To this diagonal, construct a perpendicular diagonal.
- Bisect one of the four radii.
- Draw around the middle point of the bisected radius a circular arc through the end point of the other diagonal.
- This circular arc intersects the first diagonal, upon which a radius has been bisected. Stick the compass in this intersection point and open it out to the end of the other diagonal.
- When accurately done, the line that the compass is anchored in can be marked five times as a circle chord. That is how a regular pentagon comes about in a circle. At the same time it allows the construction of a decagon.[21]

Fig. 77. A spiral figure (logarithmic spiral)

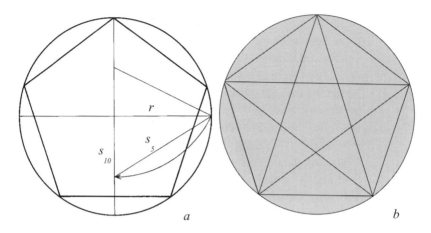

Figs. 78a–b. The construction of a pentagon

3. Basic Construction:
Erecting the Perpendicular on a Point on a Straight Line

When erecting the perpendicular in a point of a straight line, one should also refer to the construction of a perpendicular bisector. For this we choose an appropriate compass opening and mark off equal line segments from the given point, left and right on the given straight line. If we construct the perpendicular bisector for this line, then it fulfills the required conditions.

A special case occurs when the perpendicular in the endpoint of a given line segment or half-line is to be erected. If enough room is available, the line can simply be lengthened out over the endpoint so that the construction just described can be carried through. If that is not the case, then there are a series of construction aids with which the perpendicular can then be erected.[22]

Exercises about Perpendiculars
1. Construct a square whose side lengths are 2 $\frac{1}{2}$ inches. Use the construction of the perpendicular.
2. Construct a rectangle with side lengths of 3 and 1 $\frac{1}{2}$ inches.
3. With the help of the previous construction, this basic construction also allows for making a regular pentagon. Now, rather than starting from the surrounding circle, we will start from

the length of the pentagon, i.e., the pentacle side itself. Under-
lying the construction is that the pentagram and pentagon side
stand in the proportion of the *Golden Section.* The division of a
line in proportion to the medial section is elaborated upon in
the following steps (Fig.79).

- Draw the line $\overline{AB}$ that is to be divided in the proportion of the
  Golden Mean. Erect a perpendicular in an endpoint A of the
  line that has at least half the length of the original line.
- Bisect the given line.
- Transfer the bisected line attained from the common point onto
  the perpendicular.
- Connect the attained point (C) with the other endpoint (B) of
  the original line forming a right-angled triangle Δ ABC.
- Make a circular arc around the endpoint C of the short triangle
  side through the apex A of the right angle and intersect it with
  the longest triangle side. You get D. Now make a circular arc
  around B through D until it intersects the line $\overline{AB}$. You get E.
  E divides AB in proportion to the golden section.
- From the original whole line and the constructed partial line, a
  regular pentagon can now be constructed.[23] For now, the line
  $\overline{AB}$ will be put at the desired location as a pentagram side.
  Circular arcs, marked with the radius $\overline{BE}$, are made around
  both endpoints which intersect each other and the pentagram
  side. Now the figure can be finished (Fig. 80).

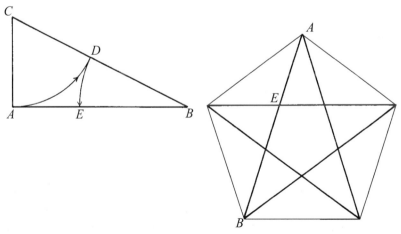

Figs. 79 and 80. Construction of the medial section and the pentagon

Use of the Set Square

The set square in common use today combines several functions: It is ruler, isosceles-right-angled triangle, and protractor all in one. It must be left up to the teacher as to when it is introduced; however it should be introduced in the proper way. If, for instance, an angle of 30° is to be drawn for which one leg and its vertex are given, then the set square should be arranged so that the middle point of the base is on the vertex of the angle and the leg that is already given lies under the 30° mark on the protractor. The second leg can then be immediately drawn along the base.

The perpendicular in a point of a line is also easy to draw with a set square. For that, the height (middle line) of the set square is placed on the given line so that the bottom side runs through the given point. Of course, one must take into consideration how thick the drawing instrument makes a line. The perpendicular can then be drawn immediately along the base.

Such drawing aids can be introduced when the actual construction steps are no longer of main importance. This goes especially for the practical demonstration of drawings for which many of the same constructions are required, as, for instance, creating a harmonic, whole figure. These kinds of drawing aids are also appropriately used in practice, as when right-angled lines are called for in technical drawing. If, however, the solution to a construction problem is asked for, so that it essentially comes down to the construction steps, then the construction should really be worked through because it reflects conceptual relationships.

4. Basic Construction: Dropping a Plumb Line

This basic exercise requires that a plumb line be dropped onto a line from a point through which the line does not run. The children are familiar with the plumb line from their building main lesson block in the third grade. It serves the brick mason by allowing for the reliable determination of vertical direction. In the first step the given line should also be *horizontal* so that the plumb line runs *vertical* (Drawing 81a). As has already been noted, the children are just now at an age when they can separate geometric relationships, such as being perpendicular, from concrete spatial positions. Therefore, the teacher must discuss with the children at length that the plumb line construction can also be carried out when the given line is no longer horizontal. One can attain a perpendicular line corresponding to a given line through the given point (see Fig. 81 b).

Construction of a perpendicular line is carried out through the following steps:

- A circular arc is drawn around a given point which meets the given line at two points.
- The perpendicular bisector is erected on the line determined by the points of intersection.

The rationale of the construction is taken from the named symmetry qualities of a circle: The perpendicular bisector on a circle chord goes through the circle middle point.

The point at which the plumb line meets the starting line is called the point at the perpendicular foot. The *length of the plumb line is* the length of the line between the starting point and the perpendicular bottom point. Sometimes this line is also referred to as the *perpendicular.*

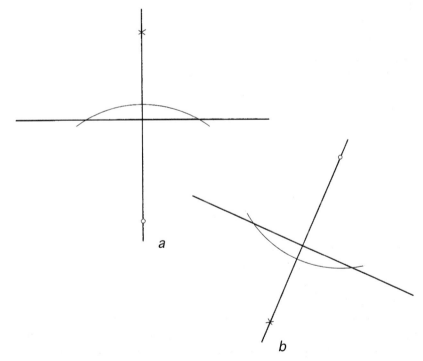

Figs. 81 a–b. Construction of the perpendicular

Perpendicular Exercise

1. Construct a square in a circle and drop the plumb line from the middle point to the four sides. Construct in this way a regular octagon.

2. Draw a regular hexagon inside a circle and drop the plumb line from the middle point to the sides. Construct in this way a regular dodecagon.

3. Construct a regular hexagon inside a circle. Emphasize the three diameters. Drop the plumb line from the endpoint of the first diameter onto the next. From the attained perpendicular bottom point drop the plumb line onto the next diameter and continue always in the same rotational direction. Then begin construction from the endpoint of one of the other diameters and continue until the construction has been carried out from all the endpoints. (If the construction is finished, then the set square can be used in the described manner to very good advantage for a further drawing – for instance, geometric drawings on calendar pages.)

4. Do the same construction as in number 3, but for four diameters whose endpoints form a regular octagon.

5. Basic Construction: Bisecting an Angle

Bisecting an angle will be taken up as the last construction that has to do with the construction of a perpendicular bisector. For this the symmetry qualities of a circle and the simplest circle figures should be considered once again: We became aware that all the median lines of a circle are symmetry axes for the circle. When two median lines form an angle, then this figure has two symmetry axes which stand at right angles to one another. They are at the same time perpendicular bisectors of the chords between the circle points of the median line. These symmetry relationships are experienced at an basic level by the children.

The children can discover the construction of the angle bisector by having once again thoroughly considered the previous figure: We start with two complete lines which form two pairs that have the same angles. The steps are: A circle with any size radius is drawn around the intersection point of the lines – the common vertex of all four angles. Four intersection points are achieved. They form a rectangle because the diagonals are the same length and they bisect each other.[24] The perpendicular bisectors on the rectangle sides are the two angle bisectors. They must stand perpendicular to one another. The neighboring angle of the two starting lines makes together 180°. Each half is 90° (see Fig. 82 a).

The construction can also be done and described with a single angle from two half-lines. This construction is to be considered as a fragment of the complete figure (Fig. 82b).

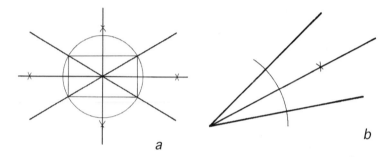

Figs. 82 a–b. Construction of angle bisectors

The following figure shows a series of straight line pairs which all have the same angle bisectors.

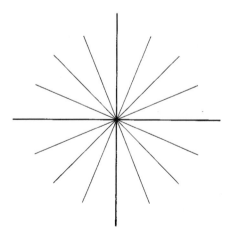

Fig. 83. Straight line pairs with the same angle bisectors

The connection between angle bisectors and perpendicular bisectors can be demonstrated using a circle: The angle bisector of two tangents (through the circle median point) is the perpendicular bisector of the chord which is determined by the associated secant.

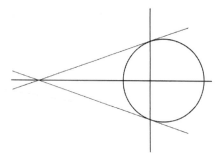

Fig. 84. The connection between angle bisectors and perpendicular bisectors shown with a circle

Exercises on Bisecting an Angle
1. Construct a square with its diagonals inside a circle. In the center of a circle bisect the angle of two perpendicular diagonals and construct a regular octagon. Construct also in this way further polygons. Which polygons were you now able to construct?
2. Construct a rectangle with side lengths of four inches and two and a half inches. Construct the angle bisectors of the four interior angles. Which figure appears in the center?
3. Draw a horizontal line and mark two points on it about six inches apart. Erect the perpendiculars of both points. Now bisect all the right angles. Bisect the angle two or three more times being careful that all the angles are the same size. Look at the figure of the interpenetrating lines in the two pencils of lines. Color in the emergent squares like a checkerboard. Much beauty can be discovered in it.

6. Basic Construction: Transferring a Line Segment

When a given line segment needs to be transferred to another place, a starting point and a direction on a line must be predetermined. In order to do this exercise the given line segment is measured by a compass and transferred to the new line from the new starting point in the predetermined direction. If the direction is not predetermined then there are two solutions (Fig. 85).

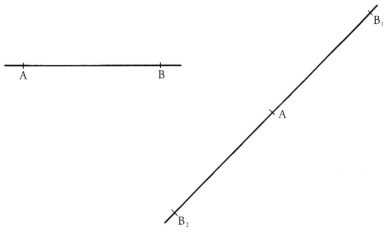

Fig. 85. Transferring a line segment

7. Basic Construction: Transferring an Angle

Often an angle predetermined by its two legs and the vertex needs to be transferred so that the vertex is put on a predetermined point and one leg upon a predetermined line or half-line. The transfer is done with the help of a compass:

- A circular arc is drawn around the vertex of the given angle that goes through both legs.
- A circular arc with the same radius and of adequate size is drawn around the new vertex.
- Now the distance between both intersection points on the legs is measured with the compass and transferred to the second drawing from the intersection point of the auxiliary circle with

the already given leg. If a direction has been predetermined then there is one solution. In the other case there are two solutions (see Fig. 86).

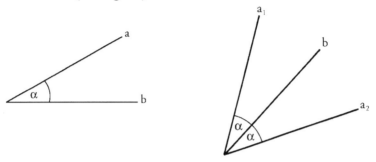

Fig. 86. Transferring an angle

In both of the previous transfer exercises the inflexibility of the tools plays an essential role. If a compass changed like a living organism when it was moved or made streaming forms like liquids and gases, then geometry in our sense of the word would not be possible. So, measurement, and with that the whole of geometry, depends upon the quality of a dead, stiff corpus.[25]

8. Basic Construction: Construction of a Parallel to a Straight Line through a Point

Even though as a general rule the parallel translation from triangles on rulers is used when drawing parallels, the children should learn to make a parallel to a given line through a point outside of itself with a compass and ruler.

For this, any auxiliary line is drawn through the point which intersects the given line. Through the transfer of one of the angles at the intersection point to the corresponding place of the predetermined point and the auxiliary line, the desired parallel can emerge (Fig. 87).

When this has been practiced, then the parallel translation with triangle and ruler can be shown. One must be careful to place the triangle that is to be moved. If the ruler is not long enough, then it can be moved along the triangle that has already been moved.

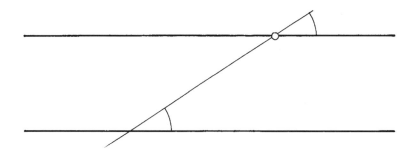

Fig. 87. Construction of the parallel

Exercises for Parallel Construction

1. Starting from a point, draw two line segments in any direction with the lengths of 4 inches and 2 inches. Complete the figure through construction of the parallels into a parallelogram. *Supplement:* Construct the angle bisectors of two neighboring angles. Construct the two other angle bisectors as parallels. Which figure forms the four angle bisectors of a parallelogram? (a rectangle)

2. Draw two intersecting lines. From the intersection point mark off equal distances on the first line and (different) equal distances on the second line. Draw through every point from one line parallel to the other line. Can you find other groups of parallels in the figure? Draw several geometric patterns.

9. Basic Construction: Constructing the Middle Parallel to Two Parallel Lines

If two parallel lines are given, then the middle parallel can easily be found in the following way: An auxiliary line of your choosing is drawn so that it intersects both parallels. The line segment between the intersection points is bisected and constructed through the middle point of the parallel as shown (see Fig. 88).

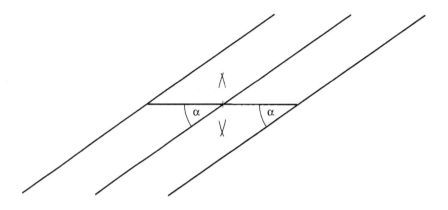

Fig. 88. Construction of the middle parallel

Middle Parallel Exercises

1. Construct a parallelogram with side lengths of 3 inches and 2 $\frac{1}{2}$ inches. Construct the center lines.
2. Construct the median lines in a square as middle parallels of the sides.

Angles of Parallels

The angles of parallels should be discussed in conjunction with the construction of parallels. If a group of parallel lines is cut from a straight line, then multiple, equal angles come about and they are described in a special way (Fig. 89).

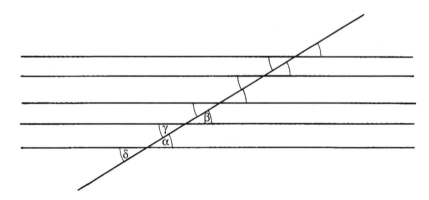

Fig. 89. Angles of Parallels

$\alpha = \beta = \delta$. α and β are called *corresponding angles*. α and γ are *alternate angles*. α and δ are *vertical angles*.

Closing Exercises

In order to use the constructions and, at the same time as practice drawing, the children can draw the most diverse *complete, regular polygons* inside a circle. Every vertex of a polygon is to be connected to every other vertex. With a high number of vertices, multiple lines go through a point which shows the exactness of the work.

The basic constructions that have been done are, generally speaking, extraordinarily well received by the children. From this activity they are exposed to much that is regulatory and organizational. During geometry main lesson blocks, I was often told about the good behavior of the class by the subject teachers. In preadolescence it is just such exercises with their effects on the psychological organism of the child that are a huge benefit.[26]

The First Meeting with the

Pythagorean Theorem

Questions about the Pythagorean Theorem[27] can be addressed with a little exercise in which the object is to find two equal quadratic areas within a quadratic area whose sum is equal to the original area. It should be a square that has been transformed into two equal-sized squares.

For this, one draws a square on the blackboard and asks who can deconstruct it so that two, same-size squares can again be made of it. Perhaps some children will have the idea to draw in the diagonals and put together the two desired squares from the four right-angled, isosceles triangle parts. To me, it seems like a good idea to have the entire figure made out of colored cardboard available in two forms: one the original uncut square and one colored and deconstructed as the triangle parts. One can then take it apart and put it together as often as one wants.

Now, with the help of compass and ruler, the children can do the needed construction themselves using cardboard. They can cut out the figure, learn to handle it with skill and finally, place it into their geometry lesson books.

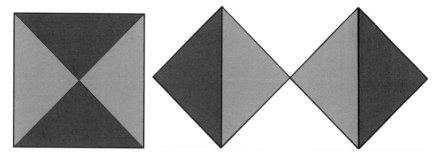

Fig. 90. The Pythagorean Theorem in simplified form

The teacher can make clear to the children the significance of the equality of the planes of the original square and the smaller squares through every possible fantasy-filled comparison. For example, one can show with pieces of pizza: Whoever gets the big piece will be just

82

as full as whoever gets the two smaller pieces. Or, the teacher can describe fields in which potatoes are to be planted. For both fields the same amount of seed potatoes are needed and one can generally expect the same amount of harvest. Rudolf Steiner's humorous suggestion to blow dust onto the imaginary potato fields, if one thinks in terms of flour, will keep the children inwardly continually active.[28]

If the children are familiar with the transformation of the square – which does not take much time – then the whole issue takes another turn: Instead of a square, one places one of the isosceles right triangles in the foreground in which the square is deconstructed through the diagonals. Now one can point out that with a right triangle, the sides, which form the right angle, are called *catheti* or sides of a right triangle and the side opposite of the right angle is called the *hypotenuse*. Then one can say aloud the Pythagorean Theorem in the special form in which the children have now encountered it:

In an isosceles right triangle, the sum of the squares of the two sides equals the square of the hypotenuse.

In connection with this probably best-known *theorem* in mathematics, the teacher can talk about Pythagoras, the man and his times.

The teacher should not fail to do the deconstruction exercise in reverse. For this one draws a not-too-large square on the blackboard and asks the class to give a square that has exactly *double* the area. Possibly there are children who will want to double the side lengths. If one demonstrates that, then it becomes clear that one has then quadrupled the square area, not doubled it. The child who erects a square over the diagonals of the small square has found the right answer. One can also formulate this into a theorem:

The area of a square is doubled when a square is constructed over one of its diagonals.

Review and Preview

With this proposed curriculum of geometry in the fourth and the fifth grades, a preparatory foundation is laid for everything that comes after. It is still not yet a logical basis, but rather an active and comparatively considered introduction to geometry. One should use it step by step to make experiences available upon which later an ordered system can be built. Whoever begins with formal presentations at too early an age, by ignoring the origin of concepts within the child, threatens to block budding interest in the world of form.

I would like to once more call attention to the fact that the symmetry experiences through the years in form drawing are of basic importance for the first geometry years. Through them, an initial structuring of the quadrangle forms is attained. They are helpful in teaching about triangles and, finally, they play a fundamental role as a reflection of illustrative geometric development. It is important to not only teach terms, laws and constructions, but also to use these things in the creation of appropriate figures. Not only provable laws belong to geometry, but also the variety of forms within which these laws are active.

Notes

1. E.A. Karl Stockmeyer, *Rudolf Steiner's Curriculum for Waldorf Schools.*
2. Rudolf Steiner, *Practical Course for Teachers*, Lecture 10.
3. The real name of this child in my class has been changed.
4. *Rudolf Steiner zur Mathematik (Rudolf Steiner on Mathematics —not yct translated into English)*, page 47.
5. New Testament Book of Matthew 27, 46; Book of Mark 15, 34; Book of Luke 23, 44.
6. See Footnote #4.
7. In the sense of projective geometry, an angle is determined by two infinitely far-off points. When we start at a finite point and think of rays going out to the infinitely far-off points, then an angle is formed at the finite point.
8. It seems appropriate here to introduce the half lines without further discussion.
9. The diameter as a geometric term has not yet been introduced. It serves here only as a reference for the teacher.
10. Likewise this has not yet been introduced as a geometric term.
11. From Louis Locher-Ernst, *Raum und Gegenraum. Einfuehrung in die neuere Geometrie,* Dornach 1988, Chapter 11.
12. Mathematically it is justified to consider circle lines as a set of line elements. A line element consists of a straight line and a point lying on that line.
13. Here it should be carefully noted that a line cannot really be defined as a set of points, but rather it is the carrier of an infinite number of points just as the point is a carrier of an infinite number of lines.
14. According to the *Waldorf School Lesson Plan*, the mathematically exact introduction to elements at infinity occurs in the tenth grade. These relationships can only be indicated here as a preparation.
15. Within the framework of projective geometry, which we always think of here in terms of general background, this certainly has a defined sense which in this instance should not be discussed yet. Here we are concerned with stimulating concrete perceptions in an elementary way.

[16] A projective labeling of lines and angles seems to be not yet helpful. It can be saved for the upper grades.

[17] Louis Locher-Ernst, *Mathematik als Vorschule zur Geist-Erkenntnis,* Dornach, 1973.

[18] Here the difference between straight lines and line segments can be discussed in more exact terms. Whether the differences in the notation – straight line AB and segment line $\overline{AB}$ – should be introduced at this point is a decision for the teacher.

[19] I would rather not yet differentiate between "interval distance" and "distance away" at this level because this difference is not part of normal language usage and is not yet required in terms of the subject matter.

[20] The first two exercises contain, in an elementary way, higher laws which will be seen again in the upper grades as logarithmic spirals. One can also point out that these forms occur in nature in numerous ways, for instance, in sunflowers or snail shells.

[21] In my opinion, one may familiarize the children with such constructions before they can be proven. One can plant future seeds that will calls attention to the fact that it will be proven at a later date.

[22] Such constructions can be given as problems at a later opportunity.

[23] Here also one should indicate that the proof will come at a later time.

[24] Cf. The House of Quadrangles.

[25] This is emphasized because in higher geometry – as already seen with perspective construction – the measure does not stay fixed in the normal sense of the word. Besides that, the interesting question arises, which geometry would befit liquids or gases?

[26] Such geometric drawings, when drawn under the supervision of a professional, can also be therapeutic, e.g. used in cases of hysteria.

[27] Cf. *The Art of Education* by Rudolf Steiner, Lecture 10.

[28] Rudolf Steiner, *The Foundations of Human Experience* (formerly called the *Study of Man*), Lecture 14.